FABER MUSIC PRESENTS

# THE ESSENTIAL POP COLLECTION

23 CLASSIC POP SONGS ARRANGED FOR INTERMEDIATE PIANO SOLO

ARRANGED BY RICHARD HARRIS

# CONTENTS





This edition first published in 2007
3 Queen Square London WC1N 3AU
Music processed by Jeanne Roberts
Cover design by Kenosha
Printed in England by Caligraving Ltd




ISBN10: 0-571-52505-9
EAN13: 978-0-571-52505-8

To buy Faber Music publications or to find out about the full range of titles available please contact your local music retailer or Faber Music sales enquiries:



Faber Music Ltd, Burnt Mill, Elizabeth Way, Harlow CM20 2HX
Tel: +44 (0) 1279 82 89 82 Fax: +44 (0) 1279 82 89 83
sales@fabermusic.com fabermusic.com

# GOLDEN BROWN

Words and Music by Jean Burnel, Hugh Cornwell and Jet Black

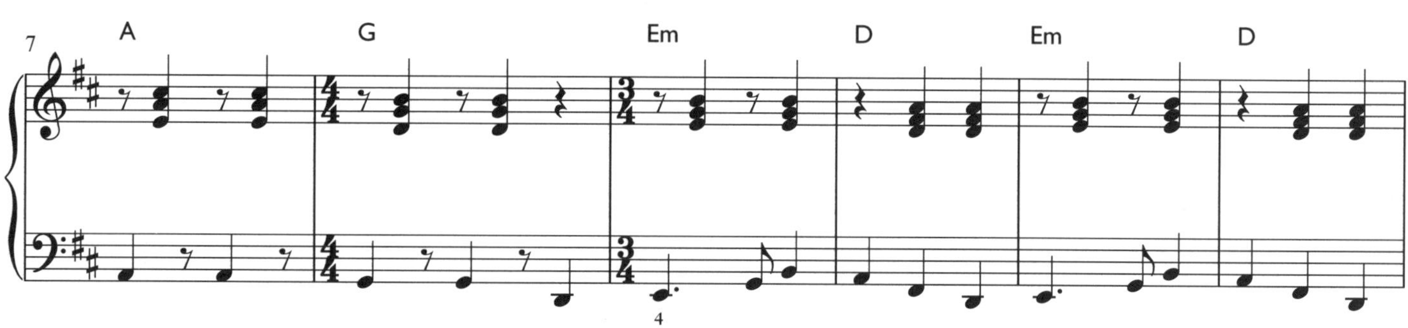


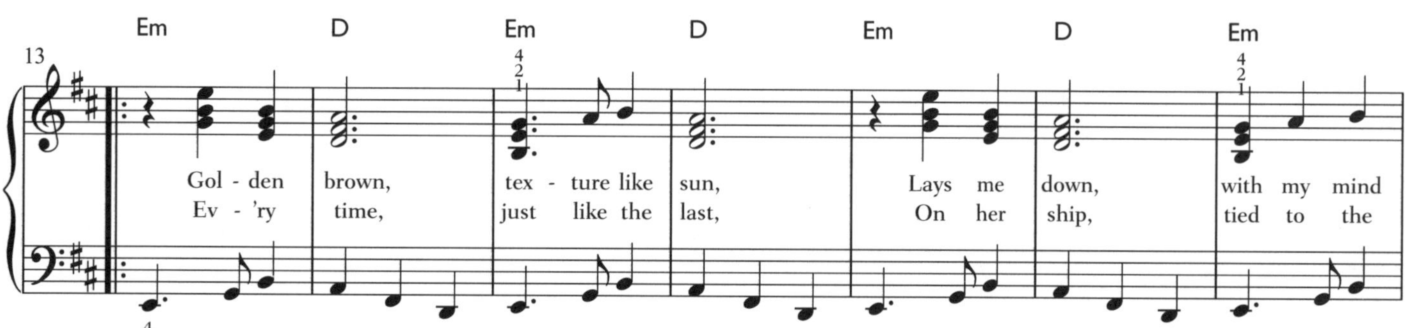


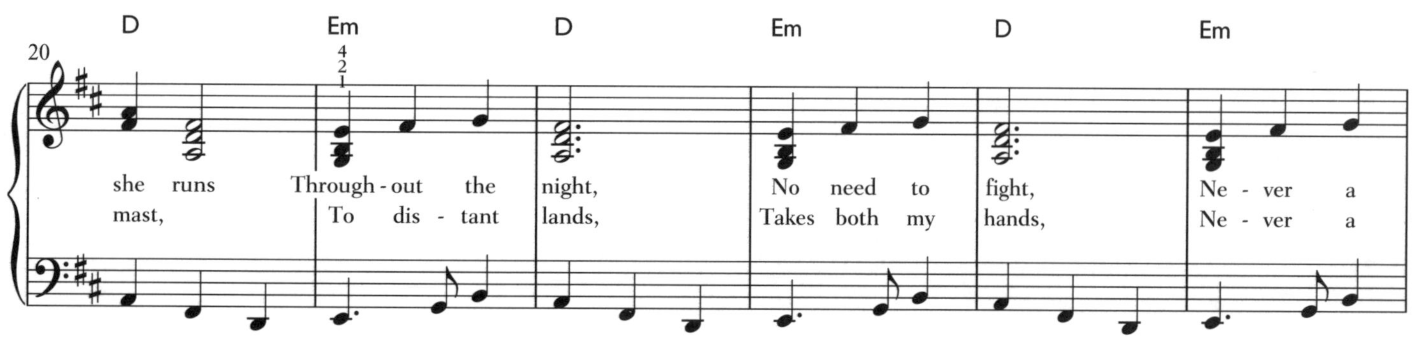

2
33
Bm
F♯m
G
D
Bm
F♯m
repeat
three times

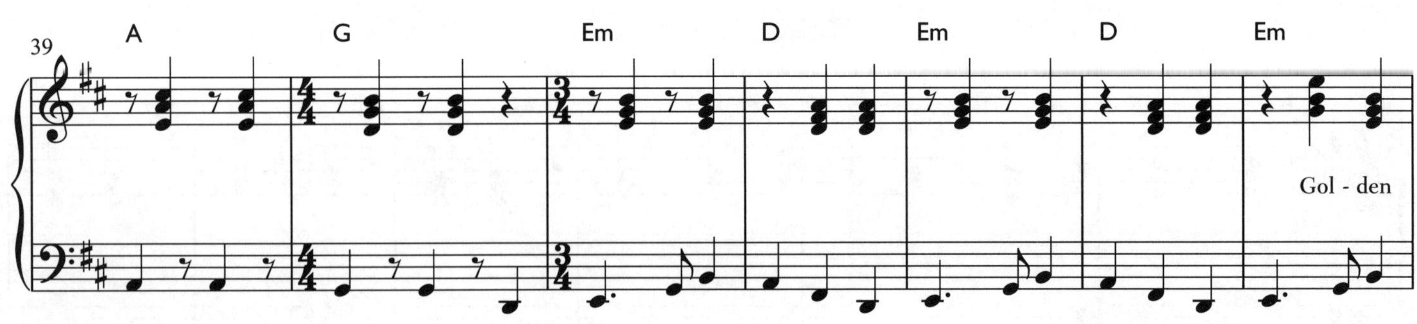
39
A
G
Em
D
Em
D
Em
Gol - den

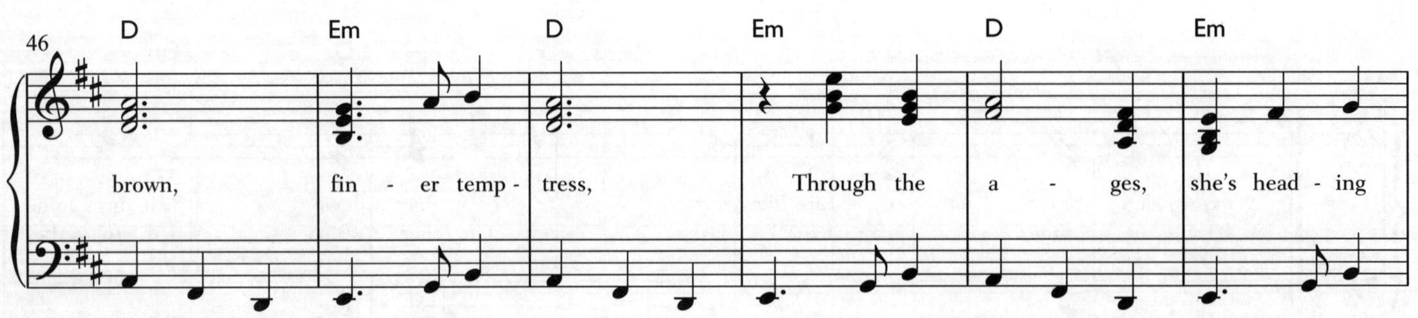
46
D
Em
D
Em
D
Em
brown, fin - er temp - tress, Through the a - ges, she's head - ing

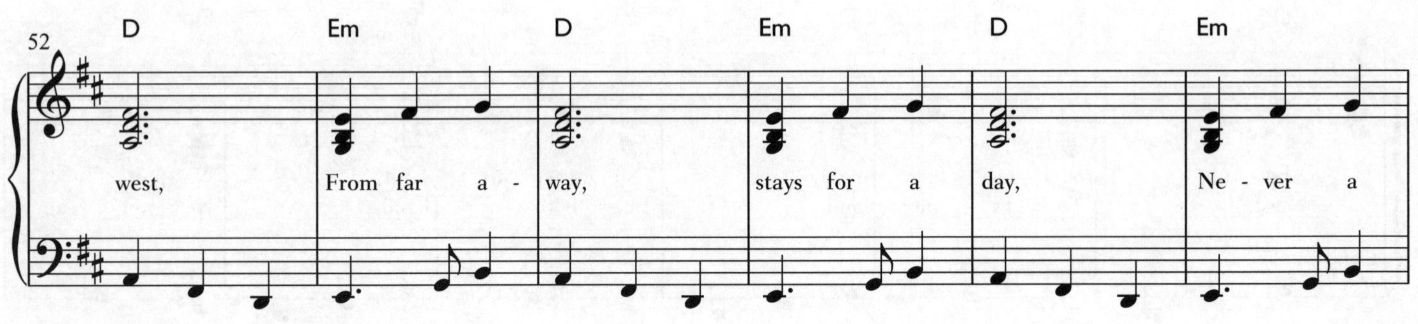
52
D
Em
D
Em
D
Em
west, From far a - way, stays for a day, Ne - ver a

58
D
Em
D
Bm
F♯m
G
frown, With gol - den brown.

64
D
Bm
F♯m
A
G
repeat
three times

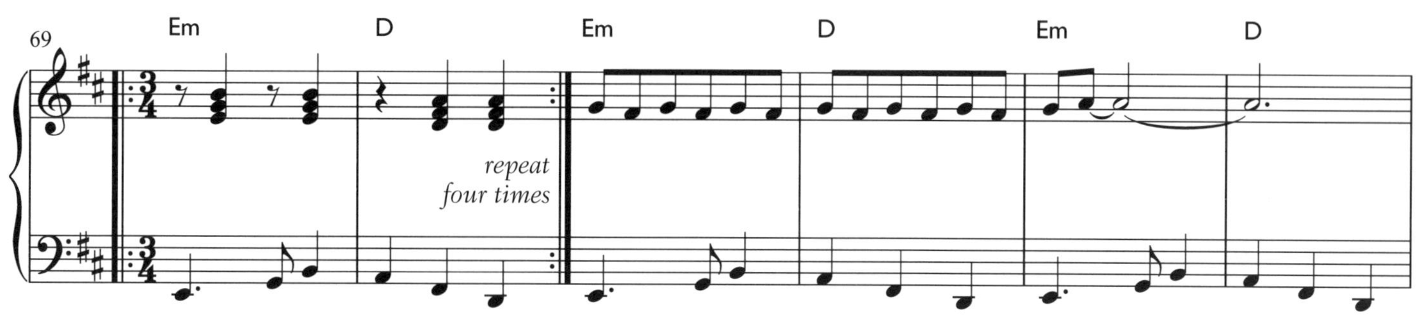
69
Em
D
Em
D
Em
D
repeat
four times

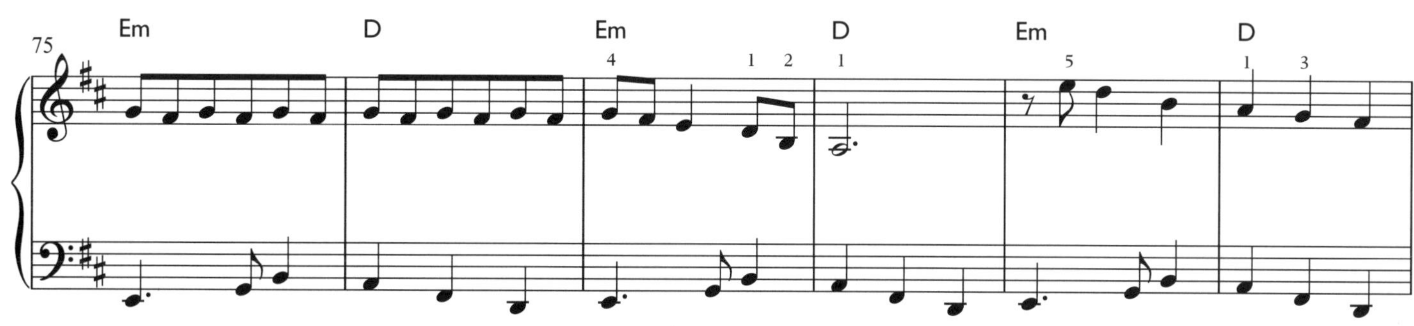
75
Em
D
Em
D
Em
D

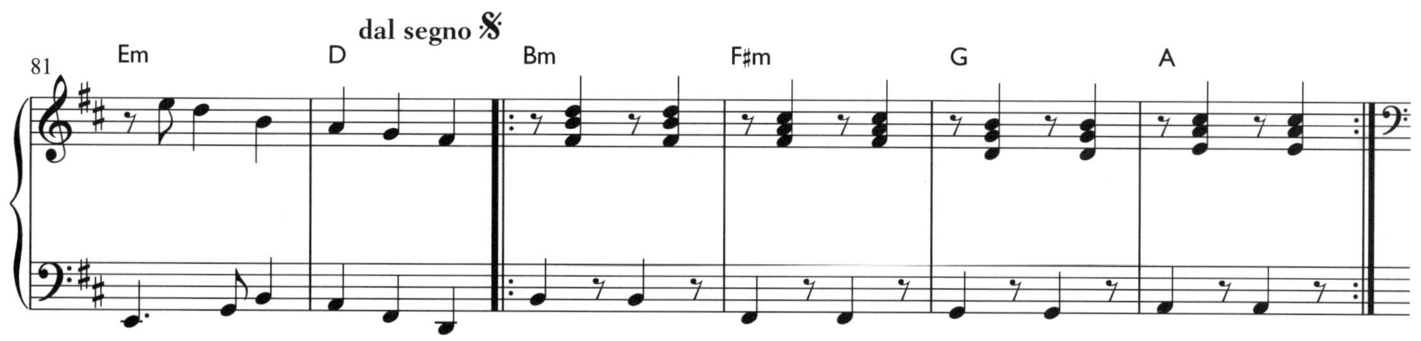
81
Em
dal segno 𝄋
D
Bm
F♯m
G
A

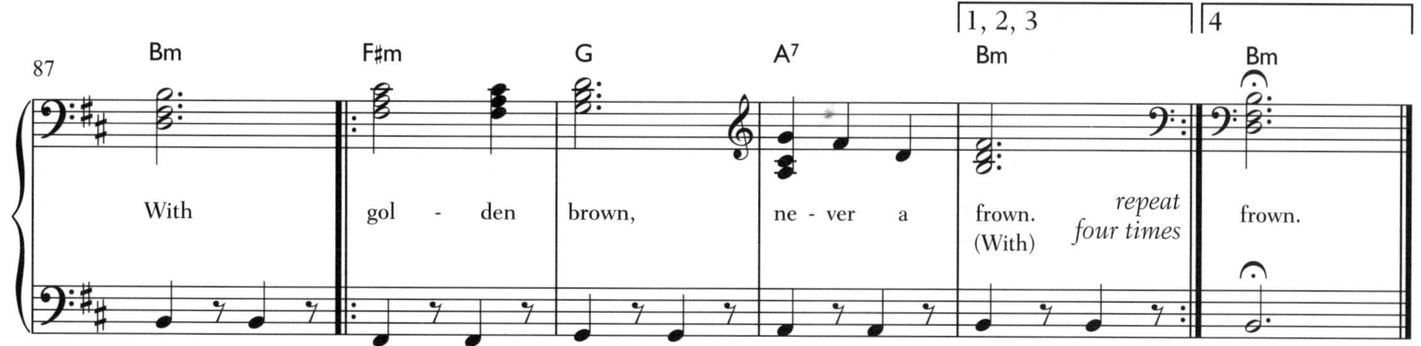
87
Bm
F♯m
G
A7
1, 2, 3
Bm
4
Bm
With
gol - den
brown,
ne - ver a
frown.
(With)
repeat
four times
frown.

# EVERYBODY HURTS

Words and Music by William Berry, Peter Buck, John Stipe and Michael Mills

26
A
Em
ev - 'ry - bo - dy cries,
com - fort in your friends.
Ev - 'ry - bo - dy cries,
'Cos
1st time continue
2nd time go to bar 52, page 8
3rd time go to bar 73, page 9
30
A
D
ev - 'ry - bo - dy hurts
Ev - 'ry - bo - dy hurts.
ev - 'ry - bo - dy hurts.
some - times.
mp
35
G
D
Some - times ev - 'ry - thing is wrong.
39
G
D
Now it's time to sing a - long When your day is night a -
43
G
D
G
- lone Hold on. If you feel like let - ting go,
48
D
G
When you think you've had too much

2nd time

52
A
F♯
Bm
cresc.
mf
Don't
throw in
your
hand.

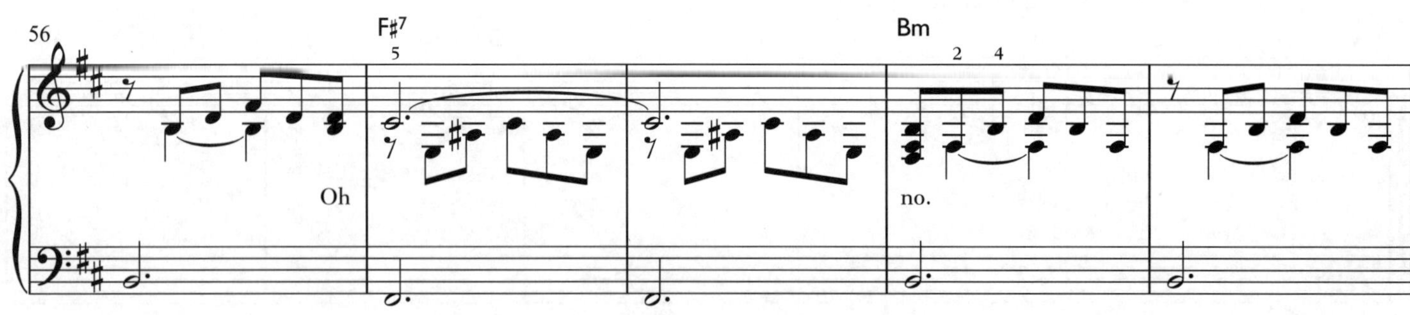
56
F♯7
Bm
Oh
no.

61
F♯
Bm
Don't
throw in
your
hand.

65
C
G
If you
feel
like
you're a
-
lone

69
C
C/B
Am
dal Segno 𝄋
(bar 5)
No
no
no,
you're not
a - lone.

3rd time

A
D
G
mp Some - times
D
G
Ev - 'ry - bo - dy hurts some - times.
D
G
Hold on. Hold on.
D
G
Hold on. Ev - 'ry - bo - dy hurts Hold
D
G
D
on. Hold on. Hold on.

# YOU'RE BEAUTIFUL

Words and Music by Amanda Ghost, Sacha Skarbek and James Blunt

A♭ E♭ B♭/D
Of that I'm sure. She smiled at me on the sub-way. She was with an-oth-er man. But
Cm7 A♭ B♭
I won't lose a-ny sleep on that 'cos I've got a plan. f You're beau-ti-ful.
E♭ A♭ B♭ E♭
You're beau-ti-ful. You're beau-ti-ful, it's true. I
A♭ B♭ E♭ E♭/D Cm Cm7
saw your face in a crowd-ed place And I
2nd time go to bar 43
A♭ B♭ Cm A♭ B♭
don't know what to do 'Cos I'll ne-ver be with you.

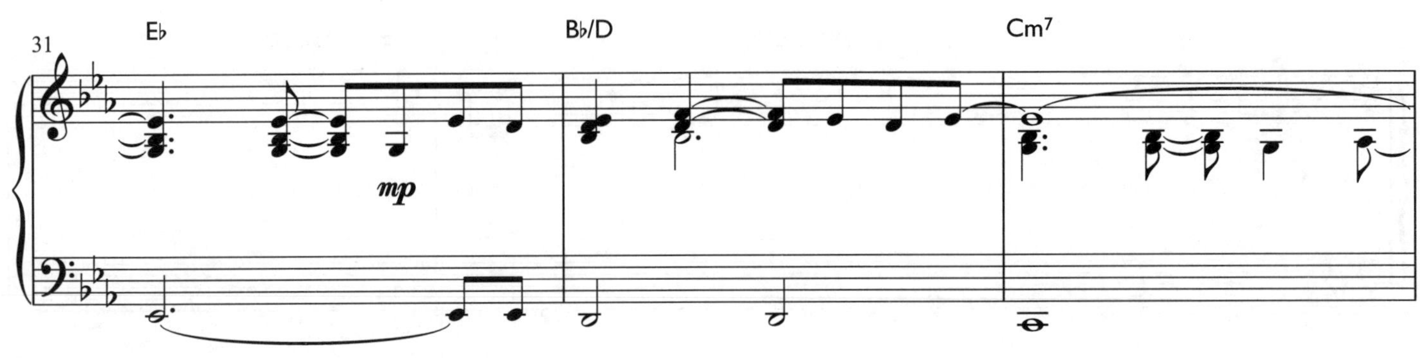
31
E♭
B♭/D
Cm7
mp

34
A♭
E♭
B♭/D
Yes, she caught my eye As I walked on by She could

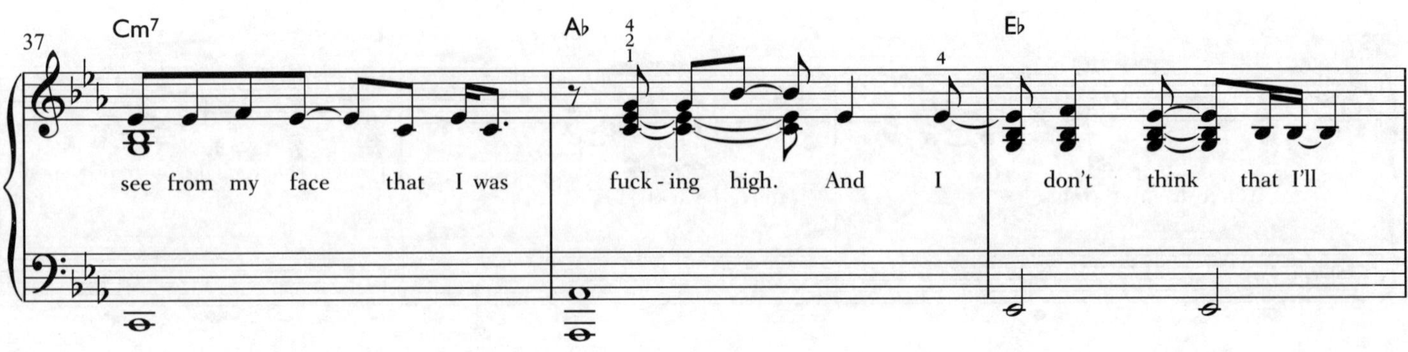
37
Cm7
A♭
E♭
see from my face that I was fuck-ing high. And I don't think that I'll

40
B♭/D
Cm7
see her a-gain, but we shared a mo-ment that will last till the end.

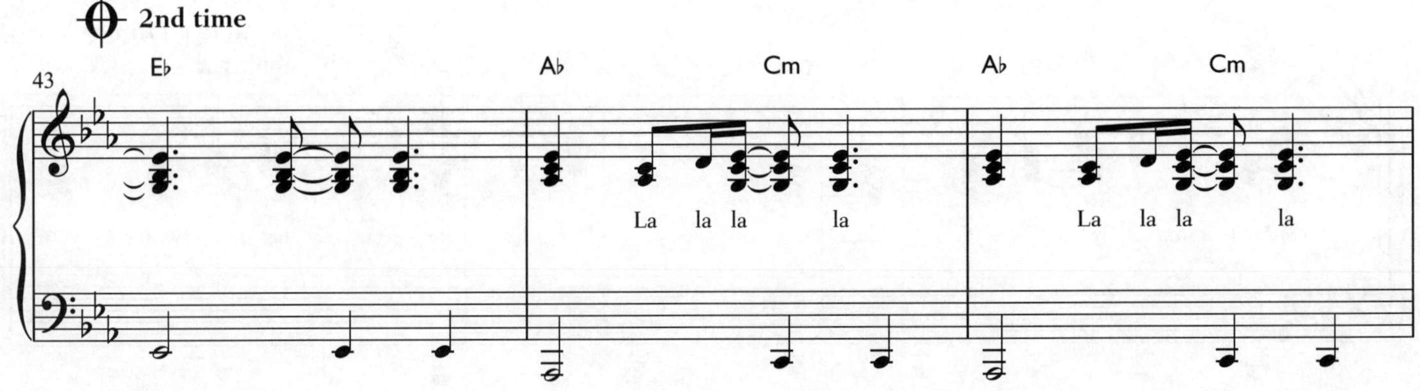
2nd time
43
E♭
A♭
Cm
A♭
Cm
La la la la La la la la

46
A♭ Cm Fm7 B♭7 A♭ B♭
La la la la la
f You're beau - ti - ful.

49
E♭ A♭ B♭ E♭
You're beau - ti - ful. You're beau - ti - ful, it's true. There

52
A♭ B♭ E♭ E♭/D Cm Cm7 A♭
must be an an - gel With a smile on her face When she thought up that I should

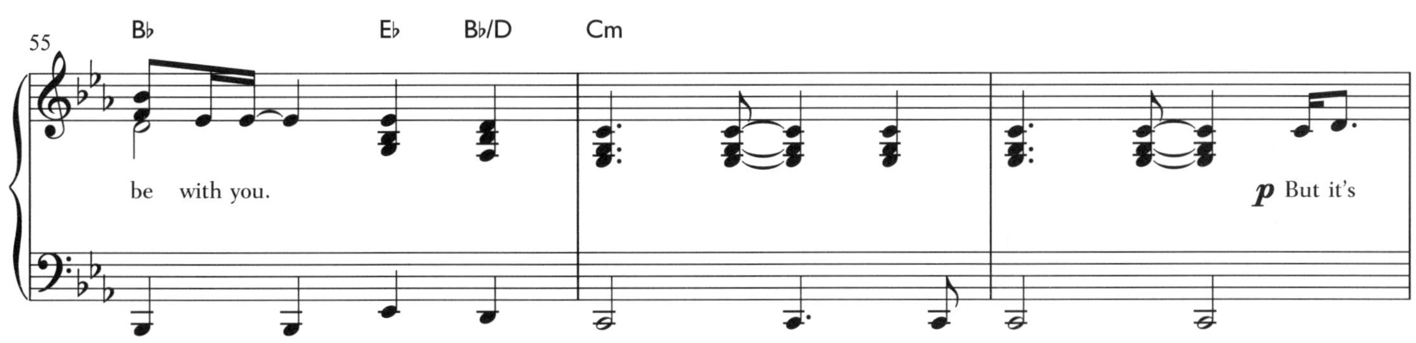
55
B♭ E♭ B♭/D Cm
be with you.
p But it's

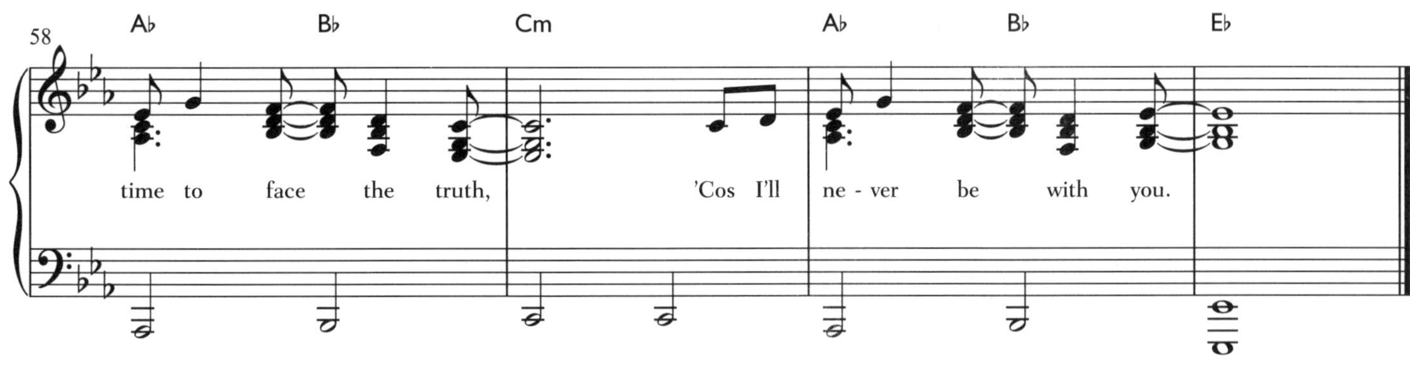
58
A♭ B♭ Cm A♭ B♭ E♭
time to face the truth, 'Cos I'll ne - ver be with you.

# DO THEY KNOW IT'S CHRISTMAS?

Words and Music by Bob Geldof and Midge Ure

27
C
F
G
hav-ing fun
There's a
world out - side your
win - dow
And it's a
31
C
F
Dm
G
world of
dread and fear
Where the
on - ly wa-ter
flow-ing
Is the
35
C
F
Dm
G
bit-ter sting of tears.
And the
Christ-mas bells that
ring there
Are the
39
C
F
Dm
G
clang-ing chimes of doom.
Well, to -
night thank God it's
them in-stead of
43
C
F
G
you.
And there
won't be snow in
Af - ri - ca this
47
C
F
G
C
Christ - mas time.
The
great-est gift they'll
get this year is
life.

52
F G C
Where no-thing ev - er grows, No rain or ri - vers flow.
56
F Dm G C F C
Do they know it's Christ-mas time at all?
61
Am G Am G
Here's to you, raise a glass to ev - 'ry-one. Here's to them un-der-neath that burn-ing sun.
65
F G C F C
Do they know it's Christ - mas time at all?
69
F C Dm7 G7 C F C F C
*f* Feed the world.
74
Dm7 G7 C F C F C Dm7 G7
Feed the world. Let them know it's Christ-mas time and
*repeat and fade*

# KARMA POLICE

Words and Music by Thomas Yorke, Jonathan Greenwood, Colin Greenwood, Edward O'Brien and Philip Selway

C
D
G
F♯7
This is what_ you get,
This is what_ you get,
G
F♯7
C
D
G
Bm
This is what you get when you mess with us.
C
Bm
D
Am
D/F♯
Em
Em/G
Kar - ma Po - lice I've giv - en all I can,
Am
F
Em
Em/G
Am
D
G
C
it's not e - nough I've giv - en all I can but we're still on the pay - roll.
Am
Bm
D
C
D
G
F♯7
This is what you get,
C
D
G
F♯7
C
D
This is what you get,
This is what you get

40
G Bm C Bm D
when you mess with us
cresc.
43
Bm D G D G D Esus4 E
mf For a min-ute there, I lost my-self, I lost my-self.
47
Bm D G D G D Esus4 E
51
Bm D G D G D Esus4 E
Oh I lost my-self, I lost my-self.
55
Bm D G D G D E Bm

# BABY CAN I HOLD YOU?

Words and Music by Tracy Chapman

21
A D Em7 G A D
right time, You'd be mine. 'I love you.' Is
mp
25
A7sus4 A7 Em7 A7sus4 A7 D
all that you can't say? Years gone by and still
29
A7sus4 A7 Em7 G A Asus4
Words don't come eas - i - ly. Like 'I love you', 'I love you.'
33
A D Em7 G D
But you can say 'Ba - by', 'Ba - by can I hold you to - night?'
mf
37
Em7 G Bm7 A D
'Ba - by, if I told you the right words, at the right time, You'd be mine.'
41
Em7 G A D Em7 G A D
'You'd be mine.' 'You'd be mine.'

# CAN'T TAKE MY EYES OFF YOU

Words and Music by Bob Crewe and Bob Gaudio

21
F♯/E
Am6/E
1
E
good to be true, Can't take my eyes off you. Par - don the
good to be true, Can't take my
25
2
E
F♯m7
eyes off you.
f
28
B7
E
F♯m7
32
B7
E
C♯7maj/min3
C♯
ff
f
I love you
36
F♯m7
A/B
B7♭9
G♯m7
ba - by, And if it's quite all right I need you ba - by To warm a
39
G♯m/C♯
C♯m7
F♯m7
B7sus4
B7
E6
lone - ly night, I love you ba - by Trust in me when I say:

43
C♯7maj/min3
F♯m7
A/B
B7♭9
G♯m7
Oh pret - ty ba - by, Don't bring me down I pray, Oh pret - ty ba - by, Now that I've
47
G♯m/C♯
C♯m7
F♯m7
D7
found you stay, And let me love you ba - by, let me love you.
51
G
Gmaj7
mf
You're just too good to be true, Can't take my eyes off you.
55
G7
C
You'd be like hea - ven to touch, I wan - na hold you so much,
59
Cm6
G/B
At long last love has ar - rived, And I thank God I'm a - live.
63
G
A/G
Cm6/G
G
You're just too good to be true, Can't take my eyes_ off you.

67
F♯m7
B7
E
f
71
F♯m7
B7
E
C♯7maj/min3
ff
76
C♯
F♯m7
A/B
B7♭9
G♯m7
f
I love you ba - by, And if it's quite all right, I need you ba - by, To warm a
80
G♯m/C♯
C♯m7
F♯m7
B7sus4
B7
E6
lone - ly night, I love you ba - by, Trust in me when I say:
84
C♯7maj/min3
F♯m7
A/B
B7♭9
G♯m7
Oh pret - ty ba - by, Don't bring me down I pray, Oh pret - ty ba - by, Now that I've
88
G♯m/C♯
C♯m7
F♯m7
B7sus4
B7
E
found you stay, I love you ba - by, Trust in me when I say.

# BLUEBERRY HILL

Words and Music by Al Lewis, Larry Stock and Vincent Rose

20
D
A
You're part of me still
For you were my thrill
24
A7
D G
1
D
2
D A
on Blue - ber - ry Hill.
(repeat as piano solo)
The wind in the
28
D
Em7 A
D
C♯7
wil - lows played Love's sweet me - lo - dy.
But all of those
32
F♯m
C♯7
F♯m
A7 D7
vows you made Were ne - ver to be.
I found my
36
G
D
thrill on Blue - ber - ry Hill,
Oh Blue - ber - ry
rall.
40
A
A7
D G
D
Hill, Where I found you.
2 3 4

# HOUSE OF THE RISING SUN

Traditional, arranged by Alan Price

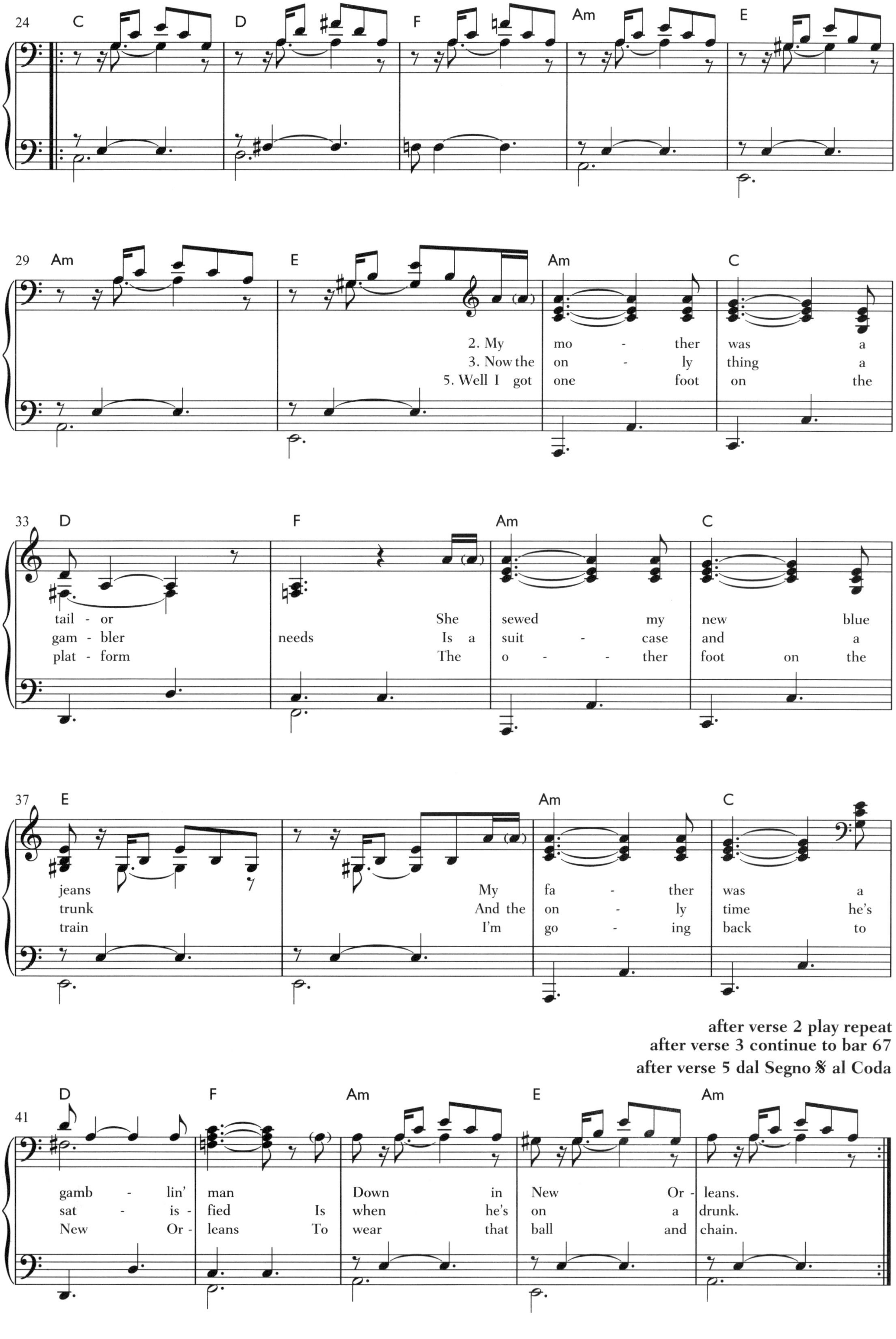

24 C D F Am E

29 Am E Am C

2. My mo - ther was a
3. Now the on - ly thing a
5. Well I got one foot on the

33 D F Am C

tail - or She sewed my new blue
gam - bler needs Is a suit - case and a
plat - form The o - - ther foot on the

**after verse 2 play repeat**
**after verse 3 continue to bar 67**
**after verse 5 dal Segno 𝄋 al Coda**

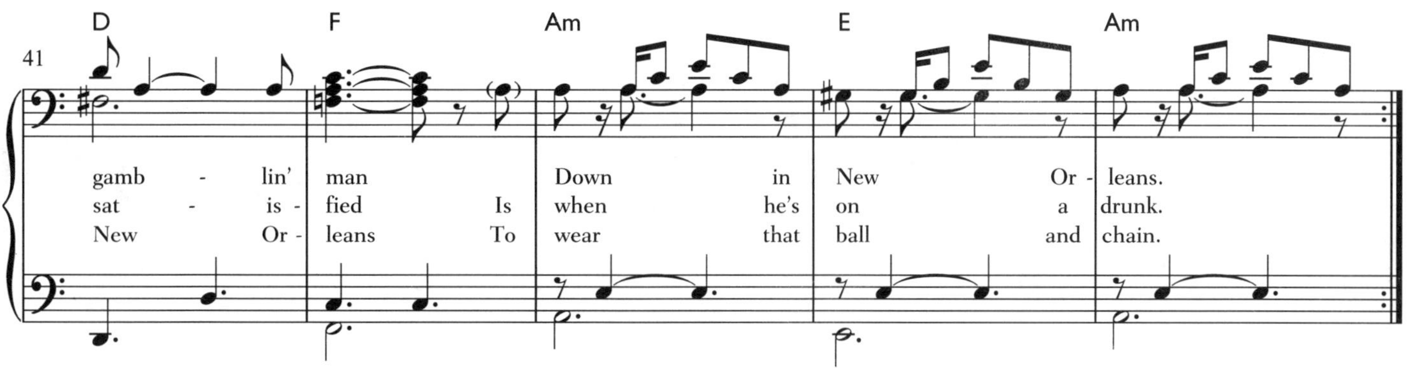

46
C
D
F
Am
E7
51
Am
E
3
Am
C
D
4
mf
56
F
Am
C
E7
1-5
Am
62
C
D
F
4
Am
E
dal Segno 𝄋
CODA
67
Am
Am
2
Dm
Am
Dm
mp
one.
3
72
Am
rall.
Dm
Am
Dm
Am7+9

# LIKE A PRAYER

Words and Music by Madonna Ciccone and Pat Leonard

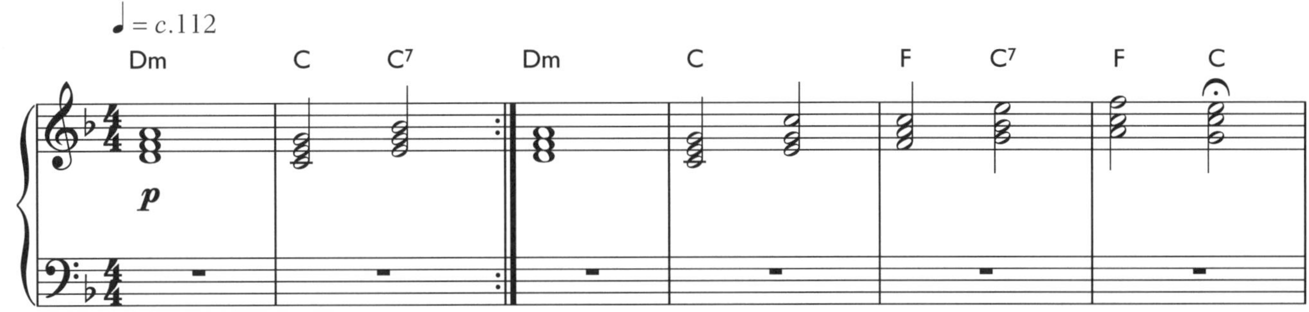


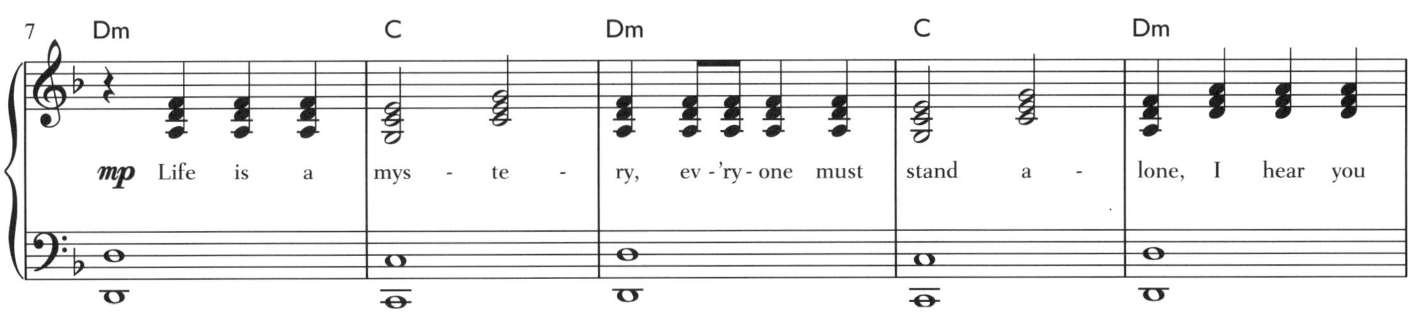


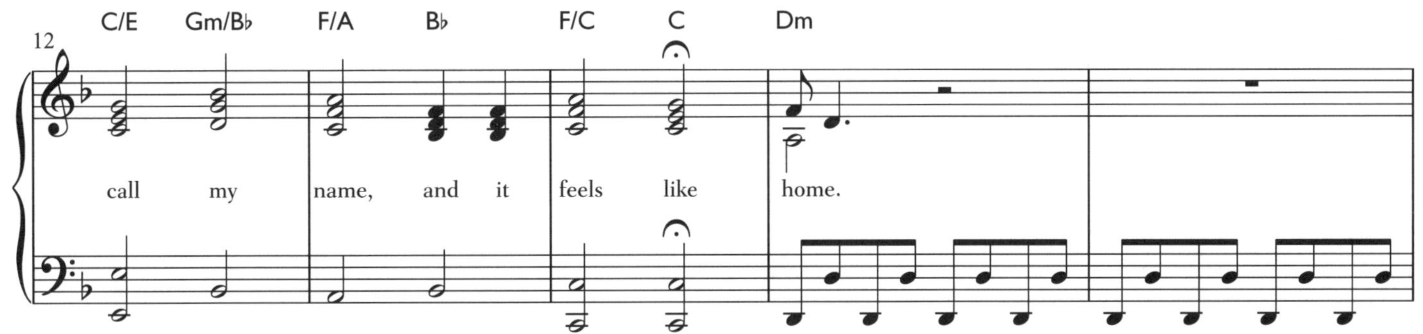

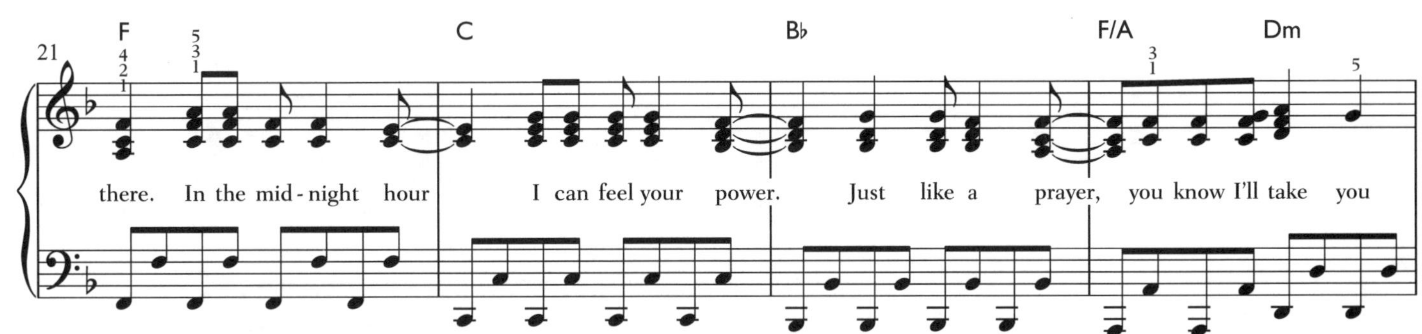

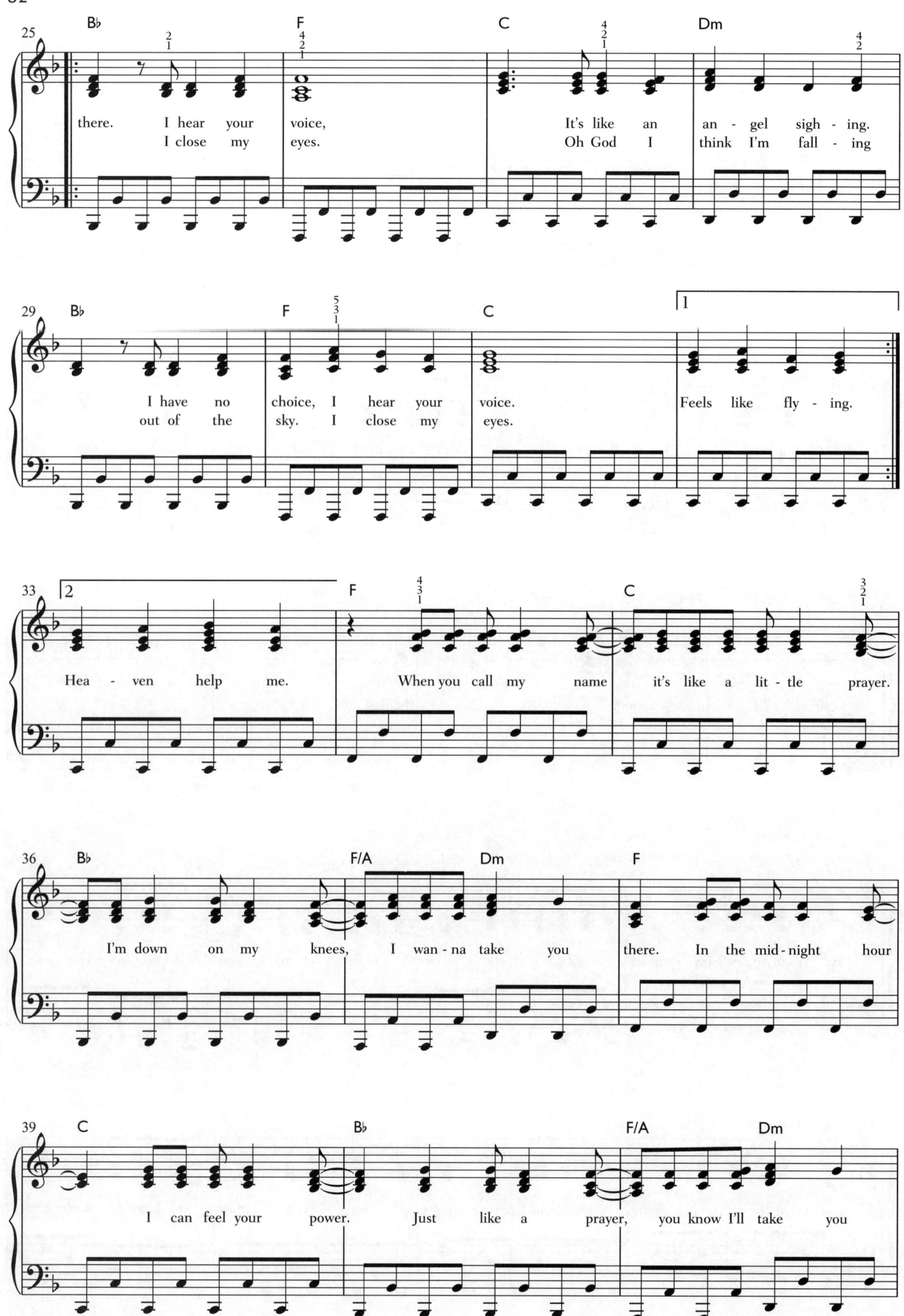
25
B♭ F C Dm
there. I hear your voice, It's like an an - gel sigh - ing.
I close my eyes. Oh God I think I'm fall - ing
29
B♭ F C
1
I have no choice, I hear your voice. Feels like fly - ing.
out of the sky. I close my eyes.
33
2
F C
Hea - ven help me. When you call my name it's like a lit - tle prayer.
36
B♭ F/A Dm F
I'm down on my knees, I wan - na take you there. In the mid - night hour
39
C B♭ F/A Dm
I can feel your power. Just like a prayer, you know I'll take you

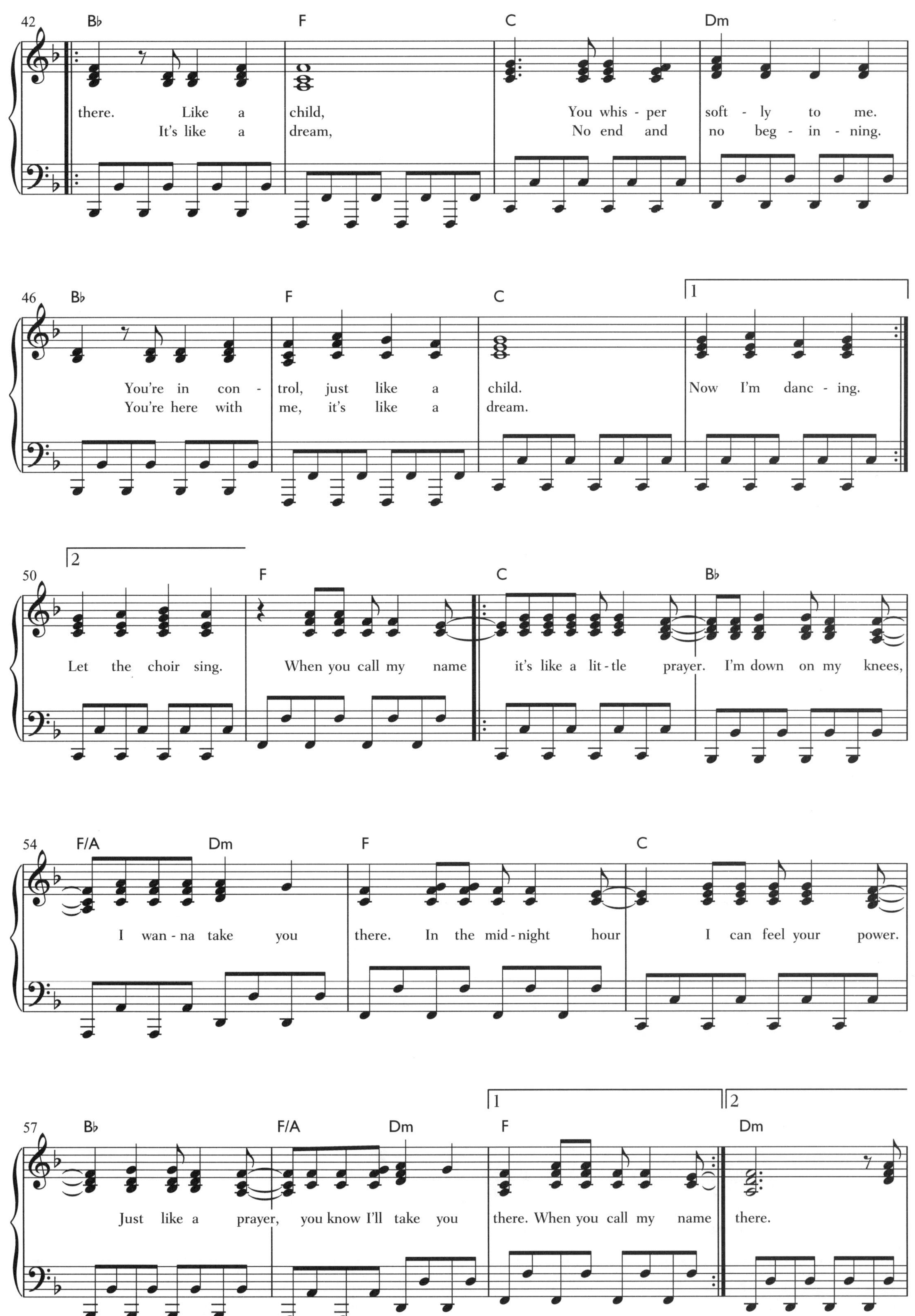
42
B♭
F
C
Dm
there. Like a child, You whis - per soft - ly to me.
It's like a dream, No end and no beg - in - ning.
46
B♭
F
C
1
You're in con - trol, just like a child. Now I'm danc - ing.
You're here with me, it's like a dream.
2
50
F
C
B♭
Let the choir sing. When you call my name it's like a lit - tle prayer. I'm down on my knees,
54
F/A
Dm
F
C
I wan - na take you there. In the mid - night hour I can feel your power.
1
2
57
B♭
F/A
Dm
F
Dm
Just like a prayer, you know I'll take you there. When you call my name there.

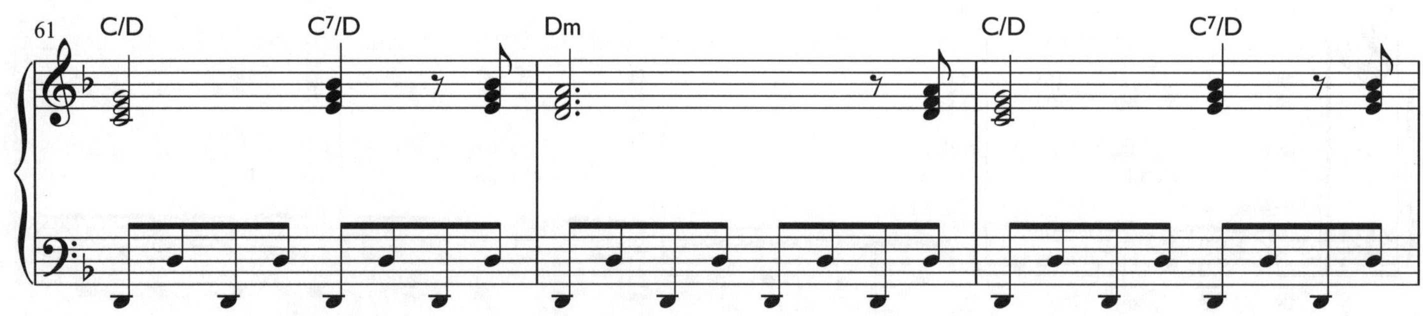
61
C/D
C7/D
Dm
C/D
C7/D

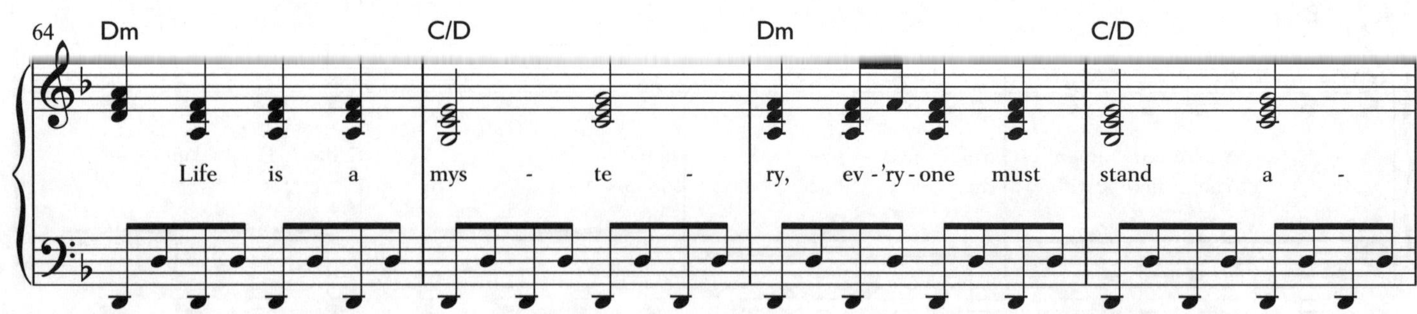
64
Dm
C/D
Dm
C/D
Life is a mys - te - ry, ev - 'ry - one must stand a -

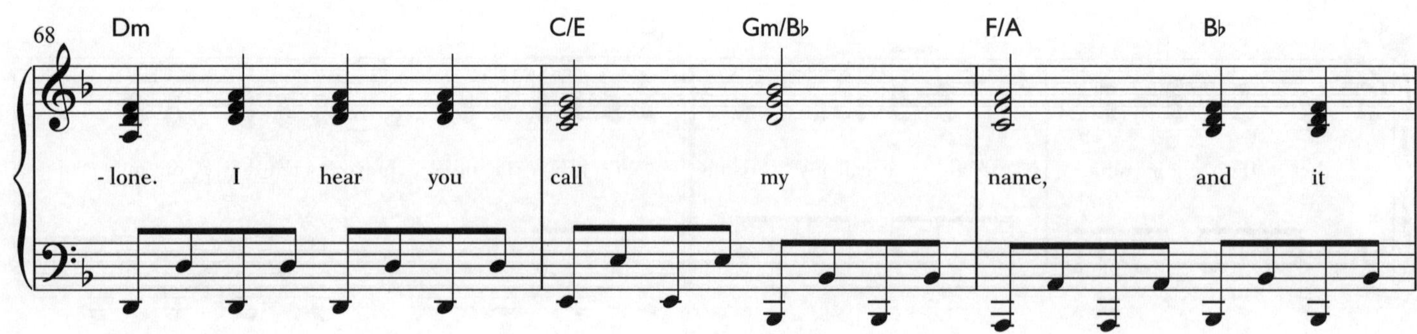
68
Dm
C/E
Gm/B♭
F/A
B♭
- lone. I hear you call my name, and it

71
F/C
C
Dm
C/D
feels like home. Just like a prayer, your voice can take me there.

74
Dm
C/D
Dm
Just like a muse to me, you are a mys - te - ry. Just like a dream

77
C/E
Gm/B♭
F/A
B♭
Csus4
C
You are not what you seem. Just like a prayer, no choice your voice can take me

80
F
C
B♭
there. Just like a prayer, I'll take you there. It's like a dream to me.

83
Am7
Dm
F
C
Just like a prayer, I'll take you there.

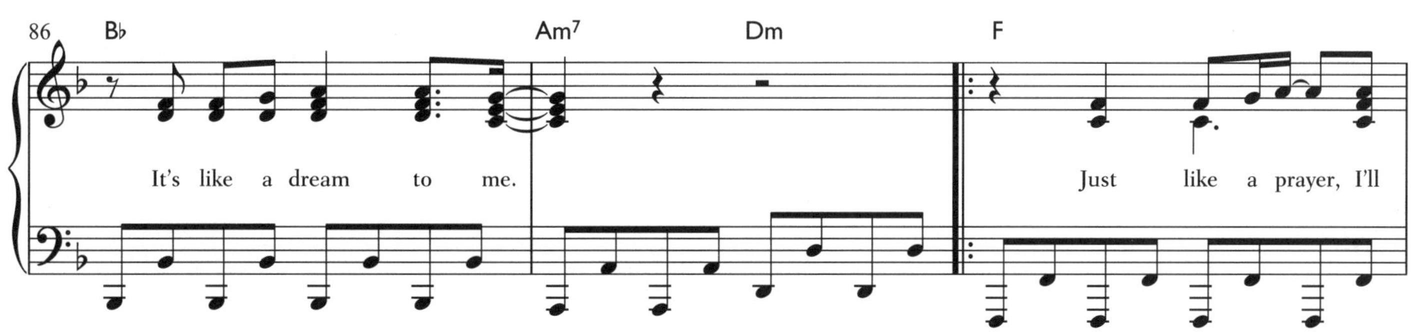
86
B♭
Am7
Dm
F
It's like a dream to me. Just like a prayer, I'll

89
C
B♭
Am7
Dm
take you there. It's like a dream to me.
repeat and fade

# LIFE ON MARS?

Words and Music by David Bowie

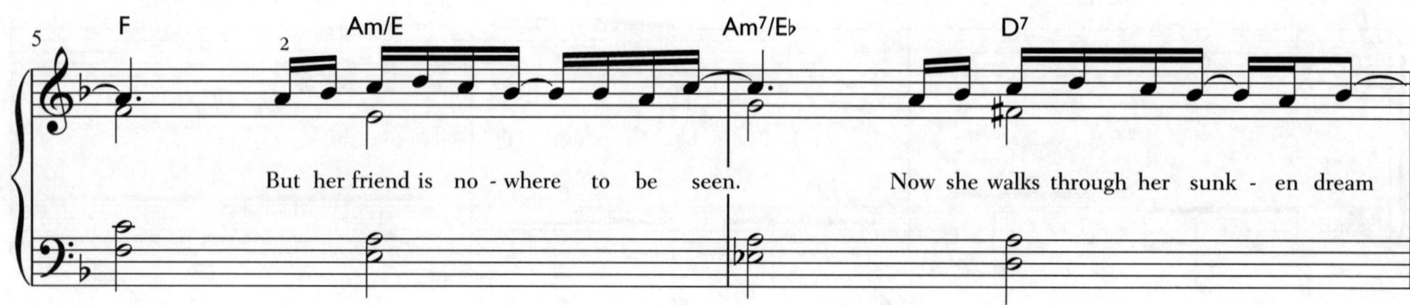


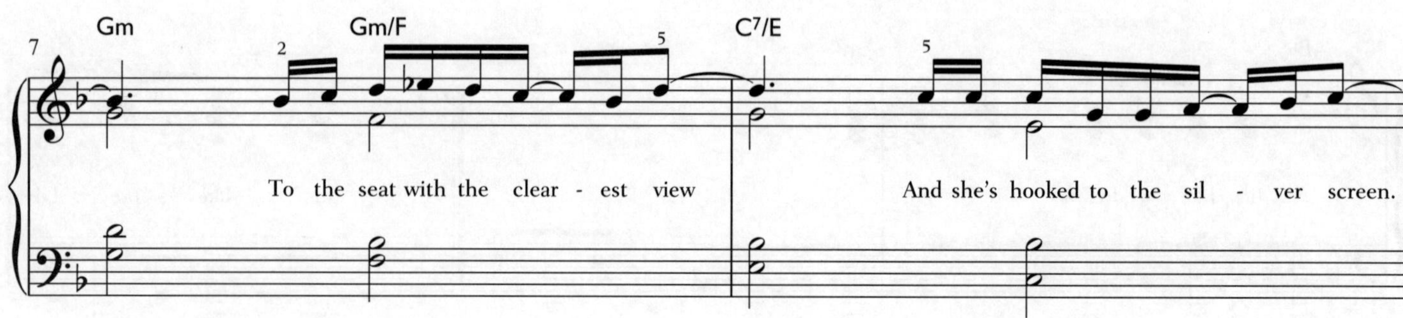

D♭
F/A
B♭m
D♭/C♭
She could spit in the eyes of fools
As they ask her to fo - cus on

B♭
E♭
Gm7
E♭m/G♭
Sai - lors fight-ing in the dance hall.
Oh man! Look at those cave - men
Law - man beat-ing up the wrong guy.
Oh man! Won-der if he'll ev - er

F
Fm
Cm
E♭m7
go! It's the frea - ki - est show.
Take a look at the
know He's in the best - sell - ing show?
Is there life on

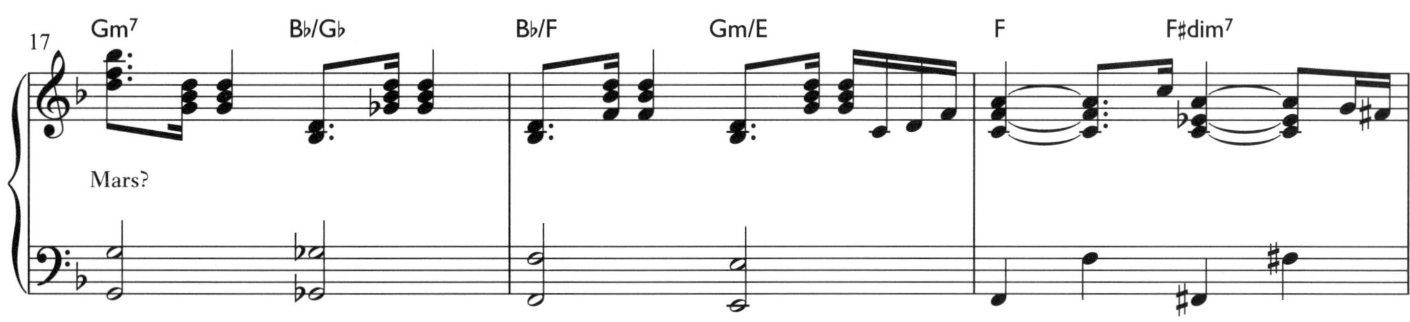
Gm7
B♭/G♭
B♭/F
Gm/E
F
F♯dim7
Mars?

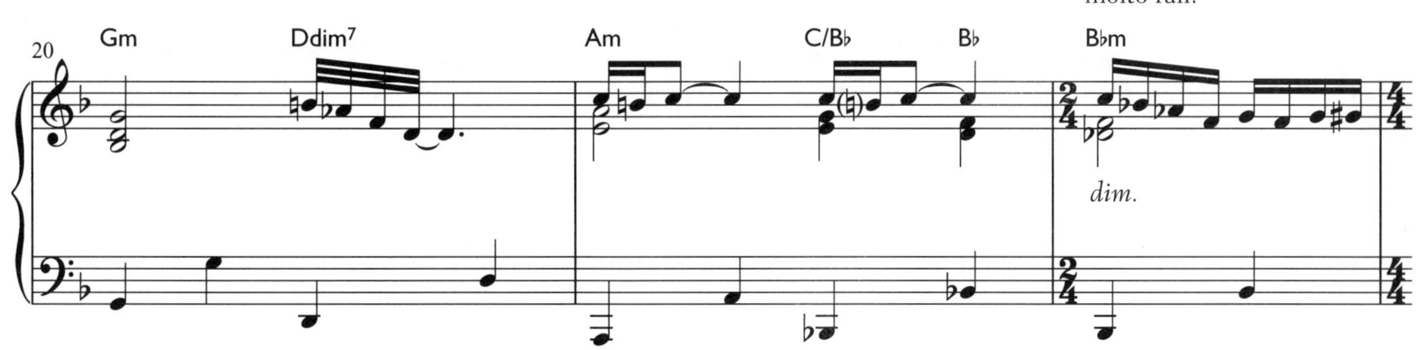
molto rall.
Gm
Ddim7
Am
C/B♭
B♭
B♭m
dim.

a tempo
F
F/E
Am7/E♭
D7
mp
It's on A - me - ri - ca's tor - tur'd brow:
Mick-ey Mouse has grown up a cow.
Gm
Gm/F
C7
Now the wor-kers have struck for fame
'Cos Len - non's on sale a - gain.
F
Am/E
Am7/E♭
D7
See the mice in their mil - lion hordes
From I - bi - za to the Nor - folk broads.
Gm
Gm/F
C7
Rule Bri - tan - nia is out of bounds
To my mo - ther, my dog, and clowns.
Cm/E♭
C/E
Fm
A♭/G♭
f
But the film is a sad - d'ning bore
'Cos I wrote it ten times or more.

33
D♭ F/A B♭m D♭/C♭

It's a-bout to be writ a-gain As I ask her to fo-cus on

35
B♭ E♭ Gm7 E♭m/G♭

Sail-ors fight-ing in the dance hall. Oh man! Look at those cave-men
Law-man beat-ing up the wrong guy. Oh man! Won-der if he'll ev-er

37
F Fm Cm E♭m7

go! It's the frea-ki-est show. Take a look at the
know He's in the best-sell-ing show? Is there life on

39
Gm7 B♭/G♭ B♭/F Gm/E F F♯dim7

Mars?

molto rall.

42
Gm B♭/F E♭ E♭m B♭

L.H.

# HANDBAGS AND GLADRAGS

Words and Music by Michael D'Abo

16
F F7 B♭ C
you my love When they have final - ly stripped you of The
19
E♭ E♭/F
hand - bags and the glad - rags that your poor old Gran - dad had to sweat to
21
B♭ B♭/A♭ E♭/G F7 B♭ B♭/A♭ E♭ E♭/F F
buy you? mp
25
B♭ B♭/A♭ E♭ E♭/F B♭ B♭/A♭
Once I was a young man And all I thought I had to do was smile.
28
E♭ E♭/F B♭ B♭/A♭ E♭/G E♭/F
Well you are still a young girl And you've borne ev - 'ry - thing in

31
B♭
B♭/A♭
E♭
E♭/F
Gm
style.
mf
So once you think you're in
34
F
F7
B♭
C7
you're out.
'Cos you don't mean a
sin - gle thing with - out
The
37
E♭
E♭/F
hand - bags and the glad - rags that your
poor old Gran - dad had to sweat to
39
B♭
B♭/A♭
E♭/G
F7
B♭
B♭/A♭
E♭
E♭/F
B♭
buy you.
mp
43
E♭/F
B♭
B♭/A♭
E♭
E♭/F
Sing a song of six - pence for your sake
And drink a bot - tle full of rye.

46
B♭
B♭/A♭
E♭
E♭/F
B♭/A♭
Four and twen-ty black-birds in a cake
49
E♭
E♭/F
B♭
B♭/A♭
E♭
E♭/F
And bake 'em all
in a pie.
52
Gm
F
F7
B♭
mf
They told me you missed school to-day.
So what I sug-gest you just
55
C7
E♭
throw them all a-way:
The hand-bags and the glad-rags that your
57
E♭/F
B♭
B♭/A♭
E♭
E♭/F
poor old Gran-dad had to sweat to buy you.

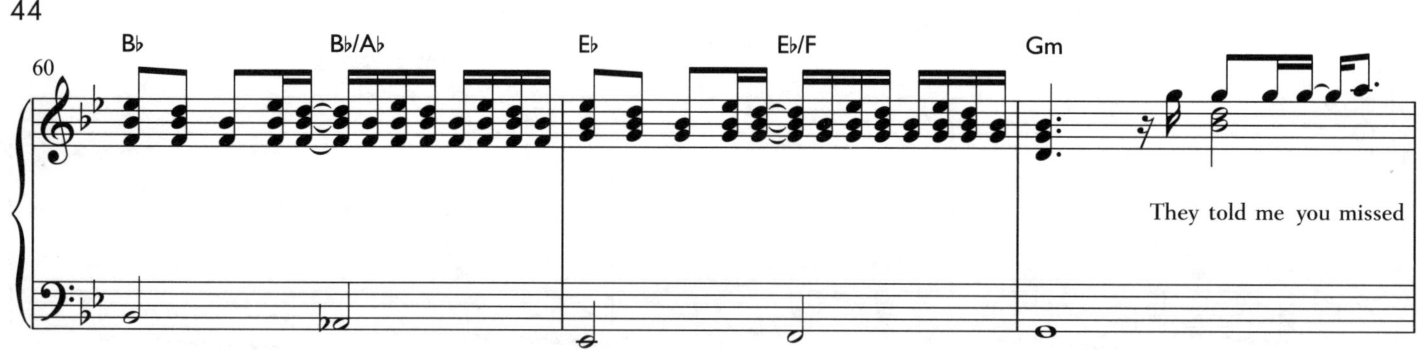
Bb
Bb/Ab
Eb
Eb/F
Gm
60
They told me you missed

F
Bb
C
63
school to - day.
So what I sug-gest you just
throw them all a - way: The

Eb
Eb/F
Bb
Bb/Ab
66
hand-bags and the glad-rags that your
poor old Gran-dad had to sweat to
buy you.
mp

Eb/G
F7
Bb
Bb/Ab
Eb
Eb/F
F
Bb
Bb/Ab
69

Eb/G
Eb/F
Bb
Bb/Ab
Eb/G
Eb/F
Bb
73

# WE ARE THE CHAMPIONS

Words and Music by Frederick Mercury

16
F7/B♭ B♭ F7/B♭ B♭ F7/B♭ B♭ C7 F Am Dm
*mf*
We are the champ - ions, my friends.

21
B♭ C F Am B♭ F♯dim7 D/F♯
And we'll keep on fight - ing to the end.

26
Gm B♭m B♭m/D♭ A/E Gdim7 F
We are the champ - ions, We are the champ - ions, No time for

**2nd time to Coda**

31
Gm7 Fm/A♭ B♭7 Cm7sus4 F Fm Gm/F
los - ers, 'cos we are the champ - ions of the world. *mp*

37
Fm Gm/F Fm Gm7/C Cm
I've ta - ken my bows

42
Gm7 Cm Gm7 Cm
And my cur - tain calls. You've brought me fame and for - tune and

46
Gm7
Cm
Gm7
B♭
ev - 'ry-thing that goes with it, I thank you all.
But it's been no bed of
49
E♭
A♭/E♭
E♭
A♭/E♭
ros - es,
No pleas - ure cruise.
I con-si-der it a
53
E♭
B♭/D
Cm
F7
B♭
chal - lenge be-fore the whole hu - man race but I ain't gon-na lose.
CODA
56
F
Am
Dm
B♭
C
F
We are the champ - ions my friends
And we'll keep on
61
Am
Am7
B♭
F♯dim7
D/F♯
Gm
B♭m
fight - ing to the end.
We are the champ - ions, We are the
67
A/E
Gdim7
F
Gm7
Fm/A♭
B♭7
Cm7sus4
champ - ions, No time for los - ers, 'cos we are the champ - ions.

# ANGELS

Words and Music by Robbie Williams and Guy Chambers

16
A/C♯
E
D
A/C♯
run - ning through my head, and I feel that love is dead, I'm lov - ing an - gels in - stead.
19
E
B
C♯m
mf
And through it all she of - fers me pro - tec - tion, a lot of love and af - fec -
22
A
E
B
- tion, whe - ther I'm right or wrong. And down the wa - ter - fall, wher - ev - er it may
25
C♯m
A
E/G♯
dim.
take me, I know that life won't break me. When I come to call she won't for - sake
2nd time to Coda
28
F♯m
D
A/C♯
E
mp
me. I'm lov - ing an - gels in - stead

31
E
E/G♯
A
When I'm feel-ing weak and my pain walks down a one-way street,
34
B
E
I look a-bove and I know I'll al - ways be blessed
37
A
B
D
with love. And as the feel-ing grows she breathes
40
A/C♯
E
CODA
E
flesh to my bones And when love is dead
mf
43
Bm7
A
E

47
Bm7
F♯m
1
E
2
51
E/G♯
B
C♯m
And through it all she of - fers me pro - tec - tion, a lot of love and af - fec -
54
A
E
B
- tion, whe - ther I'm right or wrong. And down the wa - ter - fall wher - ev - er it may
57
C♯m
A
E/G♯
take me, I know that life won't break me. When I come to call she won't for - sake
dim.
60
F♯m
D
A/C♯
E
me.
mp
I'm lov - ing an - gels in - stead.

# I HEARD IT THROUGH THE GRAPEVINE

Words and Music by Norman Whitfield and Barrett Strong

C♯m7
A7
Em7
It took me by sur - prise I must say When I found
You could have told me your - self That you love
Do you plan to let me go For the o -
A7
Em
A/E
Em
out yes - ter - day. Don't you know that I heard
some - one else. In - stead I heard it through the grape - vine:
- ther guy you loved be - fore? Don't you know that I heard
A7
Em
A/E
Em
Not much long - er would you be mine. Oh I heard it through the grape - vine.
A7
Em
Em7
Em
Oh I'm just a-bout to lose my mind. Ho-ney, ho-ney, yeah! (through the grape-vine not much
p
3rd time to Coda
F♯m/E
Em
Em7
Em
1
long - er would you be my ba - by)
2. I know a man
mp

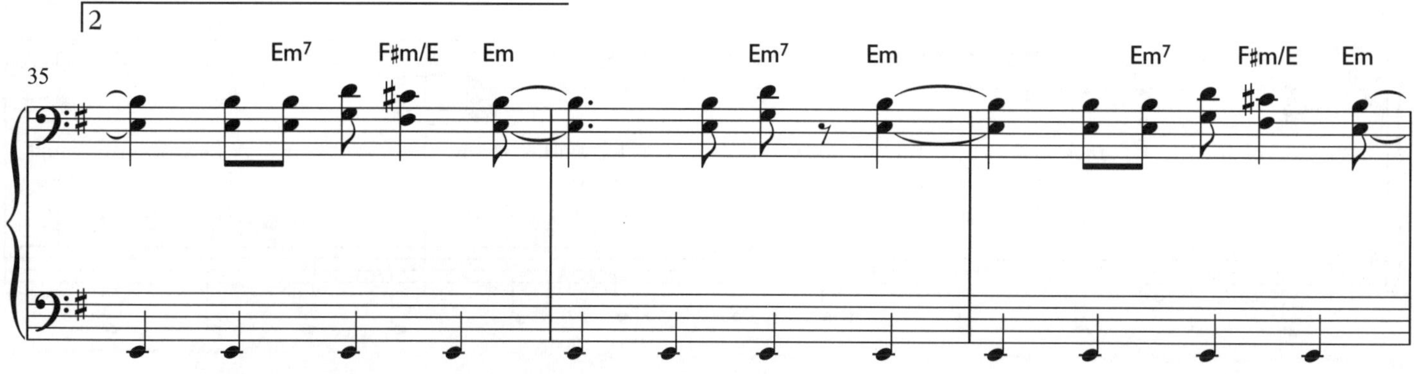
2
35
Em7
F♯m/E
Em
Em7
Em
Em7
F♯m/E
Em

dal Segno 𝄋 to 𝄌 then to Coda

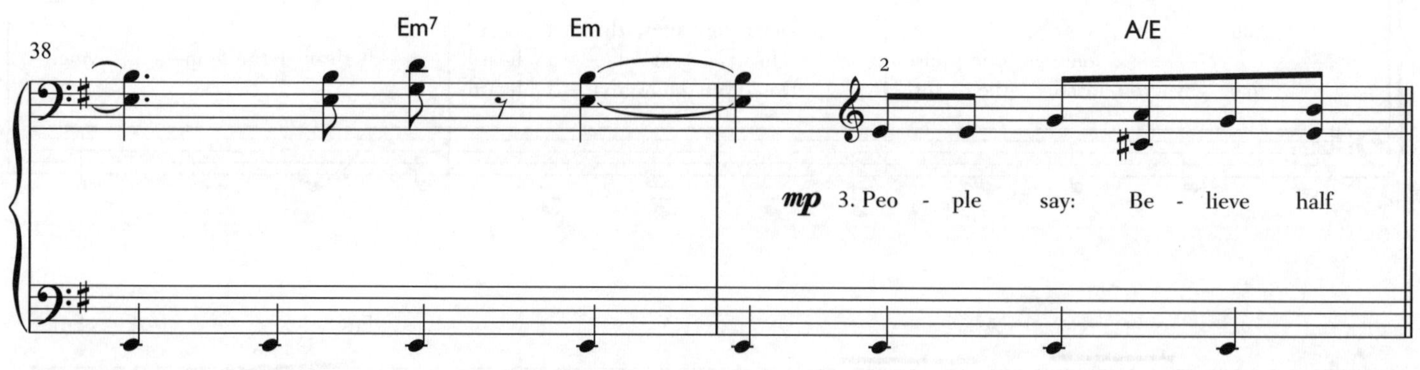
38
Em7
Em
A/E
2
mp 3. Peo - ple say: Be - lieve half

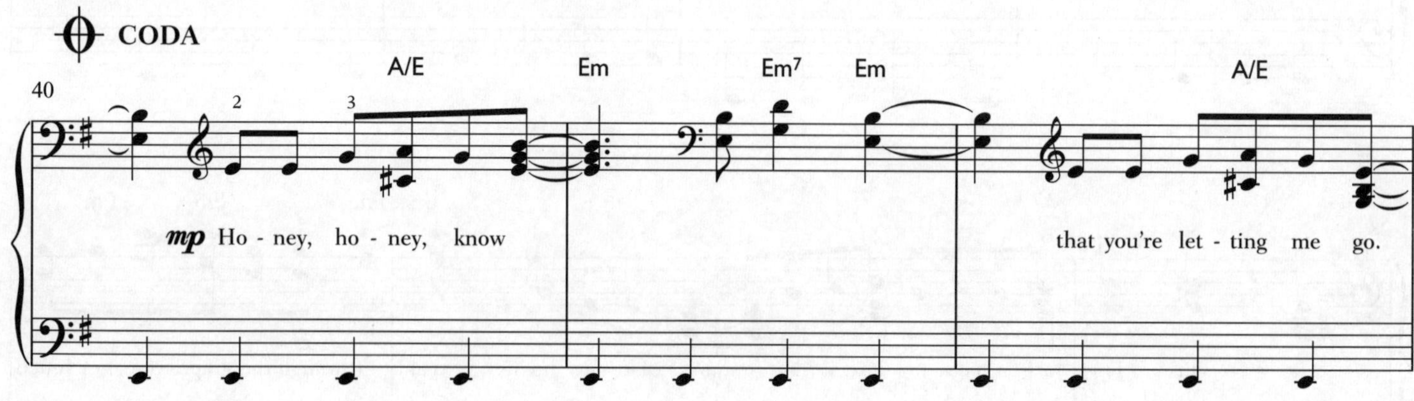
CODA
40
A/E
Em
Em7
Em
A/E
2
3
mp Ho - ney, ho - ney, know
that you're let - ting me go.

43
Em
Em7
Em
F♯m/E
Em

# I'M A BELIEVER

Words and Music by Neil Diamond

25
G C G7 C G C G C
of doubt in my mind. I'm in love. I'm a be -

30
G F D
- liev - er! I could - n't leave her if I tried. mf

34
G D G D G D G

39
D G D G C G
Love was out to get me.

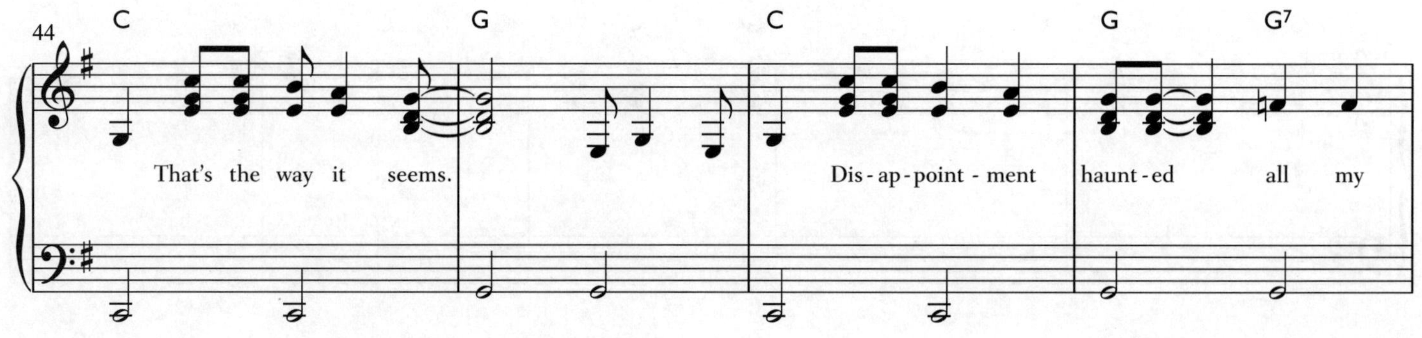
44
C G C G G7
That's the way it seems. Dis - ap - point - ment haunt - ed all my

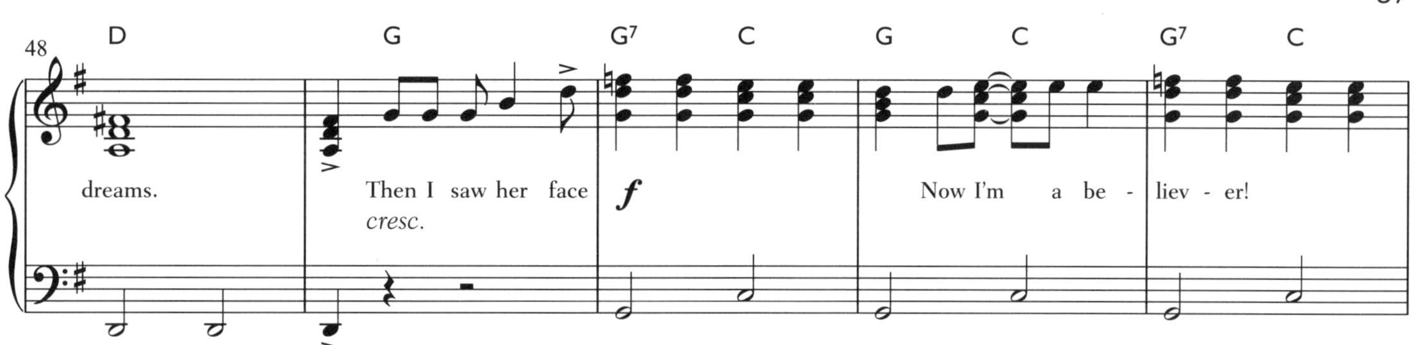
48
D
G
G7
C
G
C
G7
C
dreams.
Then I saw her face
cresc.
f
Now I'm a be - liev - er!

53
G
C
G7
C
G
C
G7
C
G
C
Not a trace
of doubt in my
mind.
I'm in love.

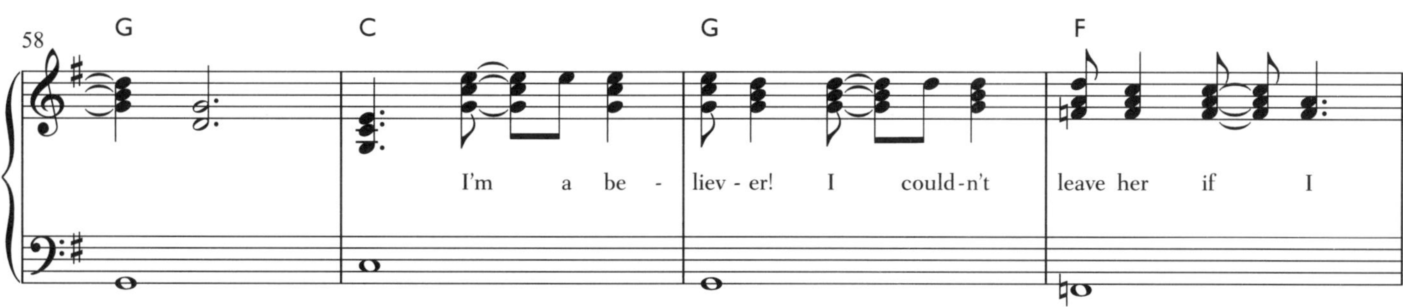
58
G
C
G
F
I'm a be - liev - er! I could-n't
leave her if I

62
D
G7
C
G
C
G7
C
tried.
Yes I saw her face.
Now I'm a be - liev - er!

67
G
C
G7
C
G
C
G7
C
G
Not a trace
of doubt in my
mind.

# (SITTIN' ON) THE DOCK OF THE BAY

Words and Music by Otis Redding and Steve Cropper

19
C
A
G
Head - ed for the Fris - co bay,
no - thing's gon - na come my way.
Sit - tin' on the dock of the bay,
22
E+9
G
E+9
Watch - in' the tide roll a - way,
25
G
A
G
Sit - tin' on the dock of the bay,
Wast - in' time.
28
E+9
G
D
C
mf
Looks like
no - thing's gon - na change,
31
G
D
C
G
D
Ev - 'ry - thing still re - mains the same.
I can't do what
34
C
G
F
D
ten peo - ple tell me to do,
So I guess I'll re - main the same.

37
G
B7
C
Sit - tin' here rest - in' my bones,
And this lone - li - ness won't leave me a - lone.
Two thou - sand miles I roamed
Just to make this dock my home.
mp
40
A
G
E+9
Sit - tin' on the dock of the bay,
Watch - in' the tide
43
G
E+9
G
roll a - way.
Sit - tin' on the dock of the bay,
46
A
G
E+9
G
Wast - in' time.
p
50
Em
G

# GREAT BALLS OF FIRE

Words and Music by Jack Hammer and Otis Blackwell

16
F7
F
balls of fire!
Kiss me ba - by!
Ooh

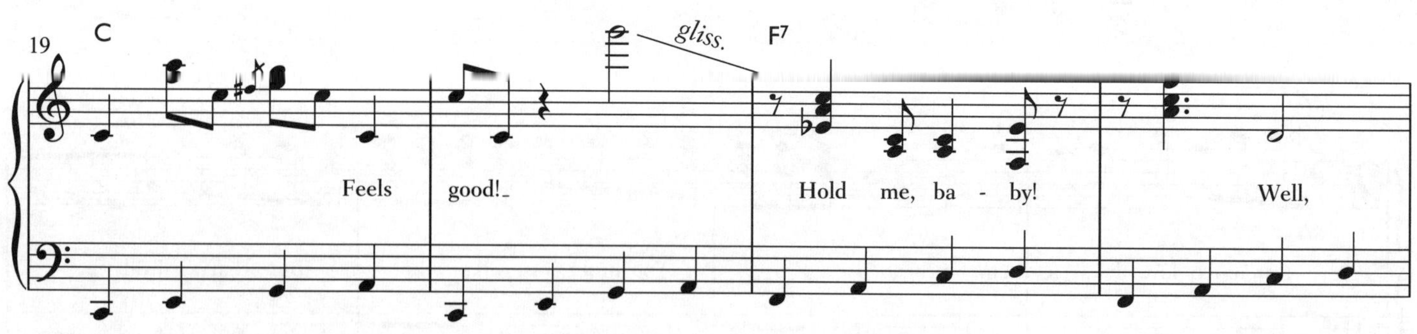
19
C
gliss.
F7
Feels good!
Hold me, ba - by!
Well,

23
G
I want to love you like a lo - ver should.
You're fine.

26
So kind.
I could tell this world that you're mine, mine, mine, mine.

29
C
gliss.
F7
I chew my nails and I twid - dle my thumbs.
I'm real ner - vous but it

32
G
F
sure is fun.
Come on, ba - by!
You drive me cra - zy.
2nd time to Coda
C
Cm
C
F7
35
Good - ness, gra - cious, great balls of fire!
39
G7
F7
gliss.
43
C
47
F7
G
F7
51
C
F7
Kiss me, ba - by!
CODA
C

# RELIGHT MY FIRE

Words and Music by Dan Hartman

18
Em7 A F♯/A♯ Em7 D/F♯ G A Bm7 A/B Bm7
But if we all stand up in the name of love And
But if we all stand up for what we bel - ieve And
21
Em7 D/F♯ G A Bm7 A/B Bm7 Em7 D/F♯ G A
state the case of what we're dream - ing of, I've got to say I on - ly dream of
may - be live with - in our pos - si - bi - li - ties, The world would be wild for the
24
Bm7 A/B Bm7 Gmaj7 Em Gmaj7 A A/B
you. But like a thief in the night you took a - way the love that I knew.
dream. So ba - by don't turn a - way, lis - ten to what I got - ta say.
27
B Em7 F♯m7 Bm7
Re - light my fire.
31
Em7 A A/B Bm Em7 F♯m7 Bm7
Your love is my on - ly de - sire. Re - light my fire. 'Cos I need
35
1
E A Bm7 A/B Bm7
your love

39
E7
A
F#/A#
Bm7 A/B
Bm7
E7
A
A#dim7
42
2
E
Em7
F#m7
Bm7
your
love, I need your love
Re - light my fire
46
Em7
A
A/B
Bm
Em7
F#m7
Your love is my on - ly de - sire.
Re - light my fire.
49
Bm7
E
'Cos I need
Oh I need
53
A
Bm7
your love.
You got-ta be
56
strong e-nough to walk on through the
night.
There's a-no-ther new
day
on the o - ther

59
side.
You got-ta have
hope
in your
soul,
Just keep on
walk - ing.
63
Em7
A
Ooh
Strong e - nough to walk on through the night.
There's a new
66
Bm7
Em7
A
Bm7
Em7
A
day
on the o - ther side.
But I got
hope
in my
soul.
Keep on
70
Bm7
Em7
Em7/A
Em7
F♯m7
walk - ing ba - by,
Keep on
walk - ing ba - by.
Re - light my fire.
73
Bm7
Em7
A
A/B
Bm
Em7
F♯m7
Your love is my on - ly de - sire.
Re - light my fire.
77
Bm7
E
Bm
'Cos I need
your
love, I need your love.

# DANCING QUEEN

Words and Music by Benny Andersson, Bjoern Ulvaeus and Stig Anderson

D/A
A
D/A
A
D/A
16
(8)

A
D/A
A
19
Fri-day night and the lights are low,
Look-ing out for the place to go

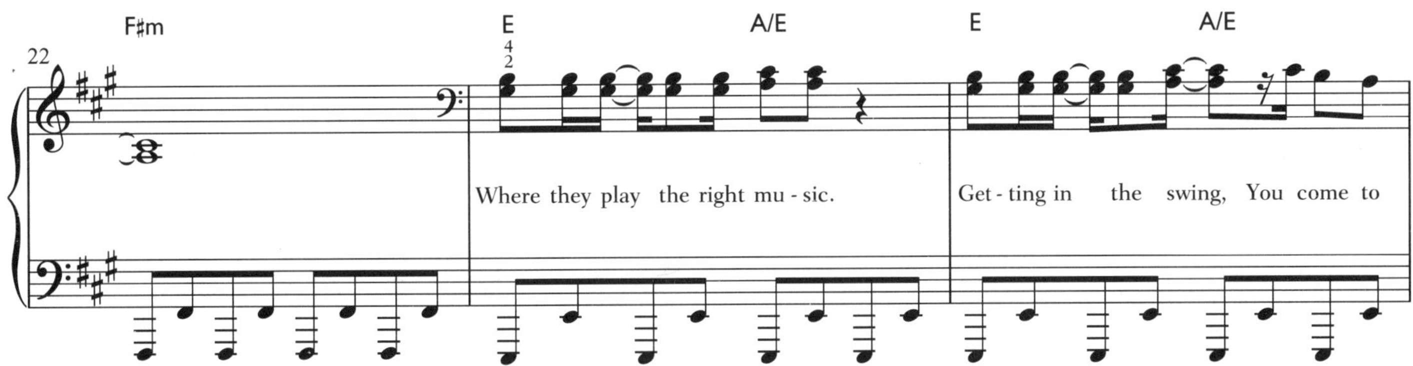
F♯m
E
A/E
E
A/E
22
Where they play the right mu-sic.
Get-ting in the swing, You come to

E F♯m
E F♯m
A
D/A
25
look for a king.
A-ny-bo-dy could be that guy.

A
F♯m
28
Night is young and the mu-sic's
high.

31
E
A/E
E
A/E
E
F♯m
With a bit of rock mu - sic
Ev - 'ry - thing is fine. You're in the
mood for a dance.
34
E/F♯
F♯m
Bm
E7
And when you get the chance
You are the
37
A
D/A
A
D/A
Dan - cing Queen. Young and sweet, on - ly se - ven - teen,
41
A
D/A
A
E/G♯
D/F♯
A/E
Dan - cing Queen. Feel the beat from the tam - bour - ine, oh yeah.
45
E
C♯7/E♯
F♯m
F♯m/E
You can dance, You can jive, Hav - ing the time of your
48
B7/D♯
E/D
E7/B
life. Ooh See that girl, Watch that scene, Dig - ging the

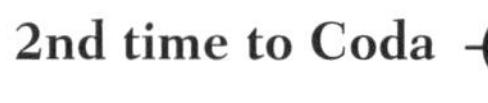


51 A D/A A 8

Dan - cing Queen.

54 D/A (8) A D/A

You're a teas - er, you turn 'em on.

57 A F♯m E A/E

Leave them burn - ing and then you're gone. Look ing out for an - o - ther.

CODA

60 E A/E D/A 8 A

A - ny-one will do. You're in the Dig - ging the Dan - cing Queen.

63 D/A A 8 D/A A

67 D/A A 8 D/A A

# BILLIE JEAN

Words and Music by Michael Jackson

2
17
Gm7
Am/G
E♭
F
Gm
Peo - ple al - ways told me, be
care - ful of what you do. Don't
f

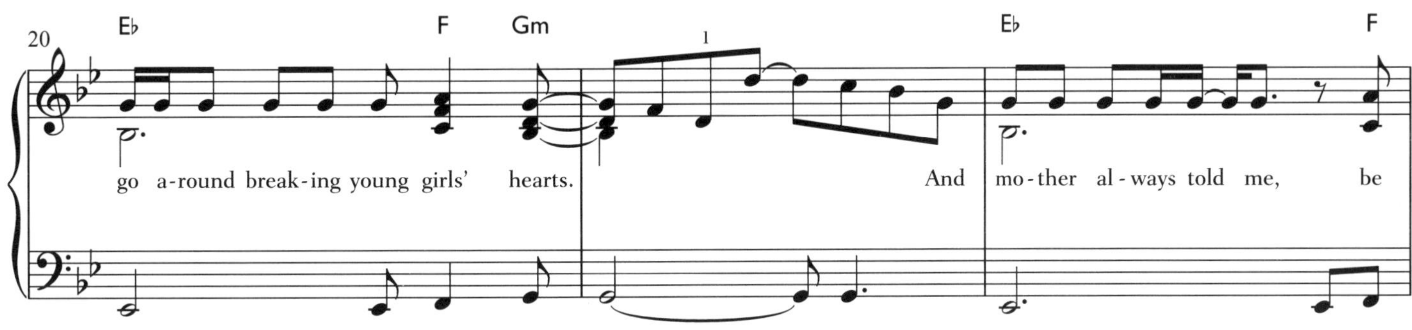
20
E♭
F
Gm
E♭
F
go a - round break - ing young girls' hearts.
And
mo - ther al - ways told me, be

23
Gm
E♭
D
care - ful of who you love, And be
care - ful of what you do 'cos the
lie be - comes the truth.

26
Gm
Am/G
Bil - lie Jean is
not my lov - er.
She's just a girl who
mf

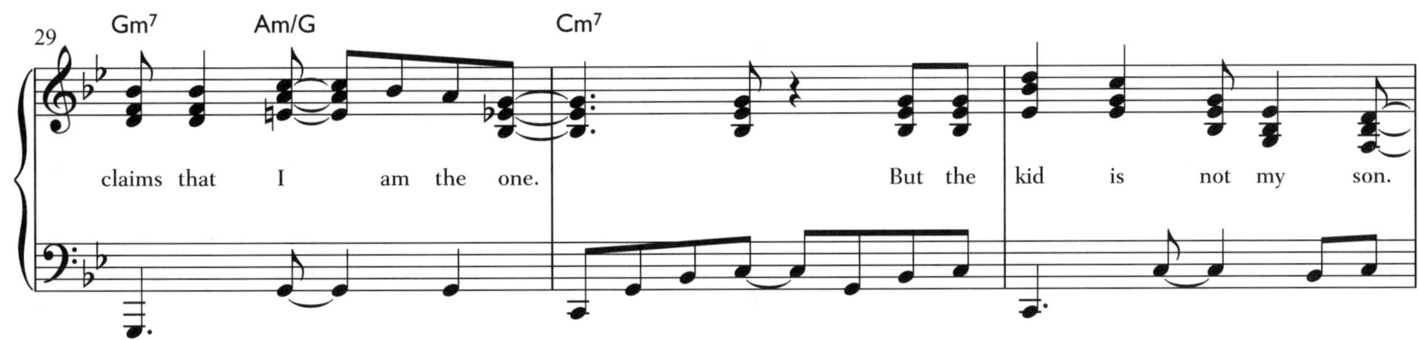
29
Gm7
Am/G
Cm7
claims that I am the one.
But the
kid is not my son.

32
Gm Am/G
Gm7 Am/G
Cm7
She said I am the one. But the
35
Gm Am/G
Gm7 Am/G
kid is not my son.
38
Gm Am/G
Gm7 Am/G
Gm Am/G
For for - ty days and for for - ty nights, law was on her side. But who can stand when she's
She told my ba - by we'd danced till three, then she looked at me Then showed a pho - to my
41
Gm7 Am/G
Cm7
in de - mand her schemes and her plans? 'Cos we danced on the floor in the
ba - by cried his eyes were like mine. 'Cos we danced on the floor in the
44
Gm Am/G
1
Gm7 Am/G
Cm7
round.
round.
So take my strong ad - vice: Just re -

47
Gm Am/G Gm7 Am/G
2
Gm7 Am/G
mem-ber to al-ways think twice.
51
E♭ F Gm E♭ F Gm
f
Peo-ple al-ways told me be care-ful of what you do. Don't go a-round break-ing young girls' hearts.
54
E♭ F Gm
She came and stood right by me, Then the smell of sweet per-fume, This
57
E♭ D Gm Am/G
hap-pened much too soon, She called me to her room.
mf
Bil-lie Jean is
60
Gm Am/G Gm Am/G Gm7 Am/G Cm7
not my lov-er. She's just a girl who claims that I am the one. But the
64
Gm Am/G Gm7 Am/G Gm
kid is not my son.
repeat four times

# LAYLA

Words and Music by Erik Clapton and Jim Gordon

last time to Coda
F♯m7 B E Am Dm B♭
You know it's just your fool - ish pride.
Turned my whole world up - side down. f Lay - la you've
And tell me all my love's in vain.
C Dm B♭ C Dm B♭
got me on my knees, Lay - la, I'm beg - ging dar - ling please, Lay - la,
C Dm B♭ C C♯m7
Dar - ling won't you ease my trou - bl'd mind?
2. I tried to give you con - so -
C♯m7
3. Let's make the best of the sit - u -
CODA
Dm B♭ C Dm
- la you've got me on my knees, Lay -
B♭ C Dm B♭ C Dm
- la, I'm beg - ging dar - ling please, Lay - la,
Dar - ling won't you ease my trou - bl'd
B♭ C Dm Dm
mind? Lay -

# WHITE FLAG

Words and Music by Dido Armstrong, Rick Nowels and Rollo Armstrong

C
Gm
I'm not try - ing to make your life hard - er or re - turn to where we were.
if you live by the rules that 'It's o - ver', then I'm sure that that makes sense.
8vb
Am
B♭
F
mf
I will go down with this ship And I won't put
Gm
Dm7
B♭
my hands up and sur - rend - er. There will be no white flag a - bove my
F
C
1
Gm
2
Gm
door. I'm in love and al - ways will be. will be. And when we
F
Am7
meet, Which I'm sure we will, All that was there Will be there still. I'll let it
Gm7
Csus4
C7
pass And hold my tongue, And you will think That I've moved on.

40
B♭
F
Gm
I will go down with this ship And I won't put my hands up and sur-
8vb

43
Dm7
B♭
F
-ren - der There will be no white flag a - bove my door. I'm in
8vb

46
C
Gm
B♭
love and al - ways will be. I will go down with this
8vb

49
F
Gm
Dm7
ship And I won't put my hands up and sur - ren - der. There will be
8vb

52
B♭
F
C
Gm
no white flag a - bove my door. mp I'm in love and al - ways will be.
8vb